FOLENS IDEAS BANK PUNCTUATION

Chris Webster

Contents

How to use this book

Ideas Bank books provide you with ready to use, practical photocopiable activity pages for your children **plus** a wealth of ideas for extension and development.

TEACHER IDEAS PAGE | **PHOTOCOPIABLE ACTIVITY PAGE**

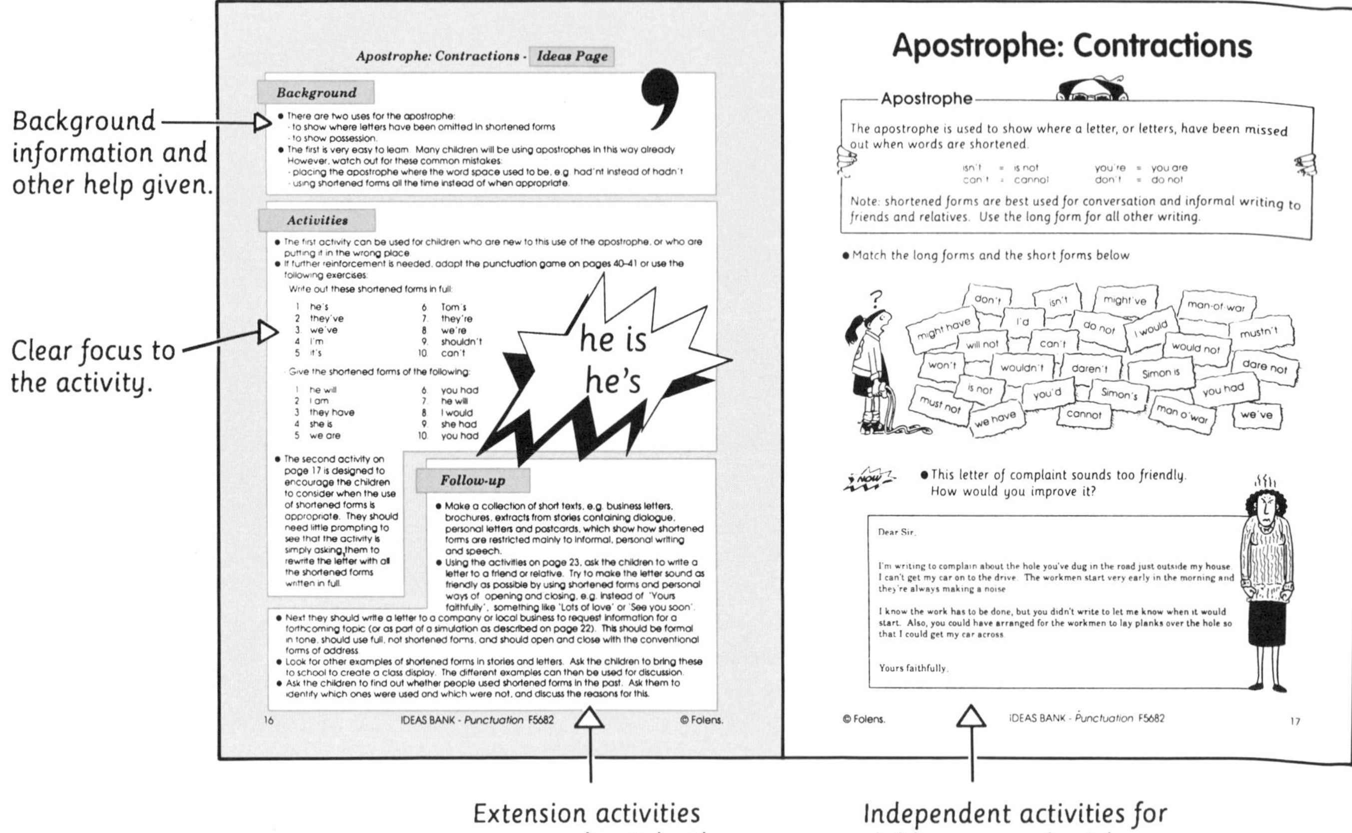

Time saving, relevant and practical, **Ideas Bank** books ensure that you will always have work readily available.

Reprinted 1997

Editor: Ian Jenkins | Cover by: In Touch Creative Services Ltd. | Illustrations by: Eric Jones

First published 1993 by Folens Limited, Albert House, Apex Business Centre, Boscombe Road, Dunstable, LU5 4RL, England.

ISBN 185276568-2

Printed in Singapore by Craft Print

Introduction

Punctuation in Context

Punctuation is just one aspect of writing. In order to make the most out of the resources in this book, it is important to bear the following principles in mind.

- Punctuation must be taught mainly in the context of children's reading and writing.
- Wherever possible real examples of punctuation, e.g. from the children's own reading books, should be used as models to illustrate specific points.
- As most classes include children with a range of abilities, teachers will need to use their professional judgement to use the activity pages with individuals, small groups or the whole class.
- The rules of punctuation vary in complexity, and so the children will learn some rules faster than others. Progression is rarely linear, and the children will need frequent reminders to use the punctuation rules they have been taught. They should be encouraged to apply these in a range of writing contexts.
- The 'templates' at the top of on the activity pages can be used in a number of ways. They can be cut out and pasted into notebooks as reminders, redrawn as large posters to form permanent reminders around the classroom, or mounted on stiff card and placed in a box in the centre of each table. In this way they can be used to reinforce basic points of punctuation in an enjoyable way.
- Both the teacher and the children should see punctuation as a tool to clarify and sharpen meaning, and as an aid to the reader, not as an end in its own right. The teaching of punctuation should be part of the broader teaching of language. For example, teaching the use of apostrophe in contractions should be combined with a study of when the use of contractions is appropriate, and teaching the punctuation of dialogue should be combined with a study of how to write effective dialogue. Above all, the study of punctuation should arise from and enhance children's own writing, and not be seen as a separate skill.

Using this Book

There are many ways of using the activity pages in this book. However, one particular method has been found through experience to be particularly effective. It satisfies the principles of good practice and makes efficient use of teacher time.

- It is a good idea to photocopy *all* the activity pages in advance (several copies of each may be needed), and if possible mount them on card and laminate them (see page 48). This creates a 'resource bank' that can save both time and money in the long term.
- The resource bank can be extended by creating additional activity pages. Answer sheets could be provided for the children to mark their own exercises (providing the process is supervised, and the exercises have simple right or wrong answers).
- When children are writing, particularly when they reach the redrafting stage, discussion with other children or with the teacher may reveal a need to improve some aspect of punctuation. The child can select the appropriate sheet from the resource bank and work through it, and then apply what has been learned to their own writing.
- At a later stage, during marking, the teacher can ask the children to practise the next appropriate activity page before progressing to the next piece of written work.
- Children should be taught independence in the use of these resources. They should know where they are stored, use them when required and replace them properly. They should be encouraged to solve their problems independently or with the help of friends, before asking for the teacher's help.
- This process should be seen as a supportive background to the production of pieces of writing which have a real purpose and audience. For example, the children may notice poorly punctuated dialogue in a story. The key points could quickly be explained using the ideas page, and they could then work through the activity page.

Why Punctuation? - Ideas Page

Background

It is an important principle of education that we try to help children understand why they are doing things. The exercises on this activity page aim to teach children to recognise the need for punctuation.

Activities

- Ask the children to work in pairs and take turns to read the passages aloud. They should then discuss the difficulties of reading the passage aloud.
- The first passage uses no punctuation whatsoever – not even spaces between words – and is extremely difficult to read. There are two lessons to learn from this:
  - space helps to clarify meaning in a similar way to punctuation marks
  - punctuation (including the use of space) is primarily an aid to the reader.
- The children may be interested to know that many ancient writing systems used capital letters only, without spaces. In some systems, e.g. runes, the writing could be left to right, right to left, or vertical. Short inscriptions were quite easy to understand, but reading longer passages was more difficult.

- The second passage is written with spaces, and is much easier to read, though the children will find that it is difficult to spot where one sentence ends and another begins.
- The third passage shows how much easier it is to read when capital letters and full stops are included.
- The fourth passage includes more punctuation and shows the effect of speech marks and the use of space (a new paragraph is used for each speaker).

Follow-up

- Ask the children to complete the story of Trevor and the dragon using appropriate punctuation.
- Provide the children with a range of reading books, from early readers to adult level, and discuss how easy they are to read and what makes them easy or difficult.
- Develop a fun activity to reinforce the main point, such as asking the children to invent their own punctuation. Give them a short unpunctuated passage and tell them to make up their own marks and insert them. Tell them not to use any of the punctuation marks they already know. Encourage them to experiment with the use of space for punctuation, e.g. a sentence on each line.
- This could be taken a step further by asking the children to invent signs to show the tone of voice in which various words and phrases could be read. In our punctuation system there are only two: the exclamation mark and the question mark. Begin by discussing what effect these have on the way we read a sentence. Ask them to invent others for loud, soft, fast, slow, happy, sad, grumbling and whispering.
- Develop this activity by discussing how actors use a range of tones of voice to bring a play to life. Give the children a short, dramatic scene and ask them first to decide how it should be performed, then to use the punctuation marks they have invented to help the actors.
- Look at some of the signs used in music to investigate any similarities to punctuation marks.

Why Punctuation?

- Read this passage aloud. Is it easy or difficult?

> trevorwaswetthroughitwaspouringwithrainandhestillhadmilestogothenh
> enoticedthecaveherantowardsitandthrewhimselfdownontothedrysandyfl
> oorhesatthereforamomentgettinghisbreathbackthenastrangesoundmad
> ehimjump

- Spaces make it much easier to read.
  Draw lines where spaces should be.
- Read some more of the story. This time it has spaces, but no other punctuation.

> the sound was a bit like a sigh and a bit like a growl trevor thought it was probably a dog or a cat sheltering from the rain like himself he walked further into the cave to find out he saw what looked like a pile of stones then with a shock that made him jump he saw two huge green eyes staring at him

> trevor stared as his eyes got used to the darkness he could see a huge dragon with green eyes and grey scales the dragon was coiled around a glittering pile of treasure coils of smoke drifted from his nostrils

- Use capital letters and full stops to make it easier to read.

- We use other punctuation marks for the same purpose – to make things easier for the reader.
  Read the next section of the story.

> Trevor did not know whether the dragon would understand, but he decided to try talking to it.
>
> "Are you a dragon?" he asked nervously.
>
> "Yes," said the dragon.
>
> "But dragons don't exist!"
>
> "I do," said the dragon.

- What makes it even easier to read?

Spaced Out! - Ideas Page

Background

This ideas page explores further the use of space as punctuation, to encourage experimentation and creativity.

Activities

- *Silence* is an example of a concrete poem. Concrete poems are as much visual as verbal and make full use of the space available on the page. The shape poems referred to are examples of another form of concrete poem. The children will quickly grasp the idea from the examples and can then experiment freely.
- Free verse makes use of space in a less extreme form, one effect of which is to make the reader pause before starting a new line. The lines are sometimes laid out to reinforce the meaning of the words, in a similar way to concrete poetry. Some free verse poems use no punctuation at all. The poet e e cummings does not even use capital letters. Writing free verse can be a creative way of giving the children a rest from the pedantic requirements of punctuation!

Follow-up

- Encourage the children to use space more effectively in their own work. Here are some points to look for:
  - is there a sufficient margin (about two centimetres) all around each piece of writing?
  - is the title set out clearly and separated from the text by at least one blank line?
  - is the line spacing appropriate?
  - are pictures neatly fitted into the text, perhaps in boxes?

  It may help to produce some standard guidelines for page layout which include margins, a title line and a date line, as well as lines for the main text.
- The children can explore the theme of space by browsing through a wide range of books, magazines, leaflets and newspapers. Here are some aspects they might consider:
  - margins of white space surround the pages of a printed book – ask them to consider the proportions of the margins and the importance of margins in their own work
  - the way spacing, lines and boxes are used to make different sections of text stand out in a non-fiction book, magazine or newspaper
  - a long piece of writing is divided into paragraphs to make it easier to understand (non-fiction books often have sub-headings for each paragraph)
  - dialogue is set out with a new line for each new speaker to make it easier to read
  - addresses are spaced out to be quick and easy to read.
- The idea that space influences meaning and improves legibility in a similar way to punctuation can be reinforced by playing the code game. This involves experimenting with the spaces between words in order to make them much more difficult to read. The code on the gravestone in this example is quite easy to crack, but it is surprising how difficult it can seem until the children realise that the spaces between the words have been altered. When they have grasped this they can then go on to write their own coded messages for their friends to decipher.

Spaced Out!

- Explain how this poem works.

Silence silence silence
Silence silence
Silence silence silence

- Write a similar poem using the ideas of loneliness and emptiness.

Some modern poems use the space on the page instead of punctuation.

Autumn leaves
firecracker colours
red and yellow and gold
falling
falling
falling
to the ground

Some, called shape poems, are even more unusual.

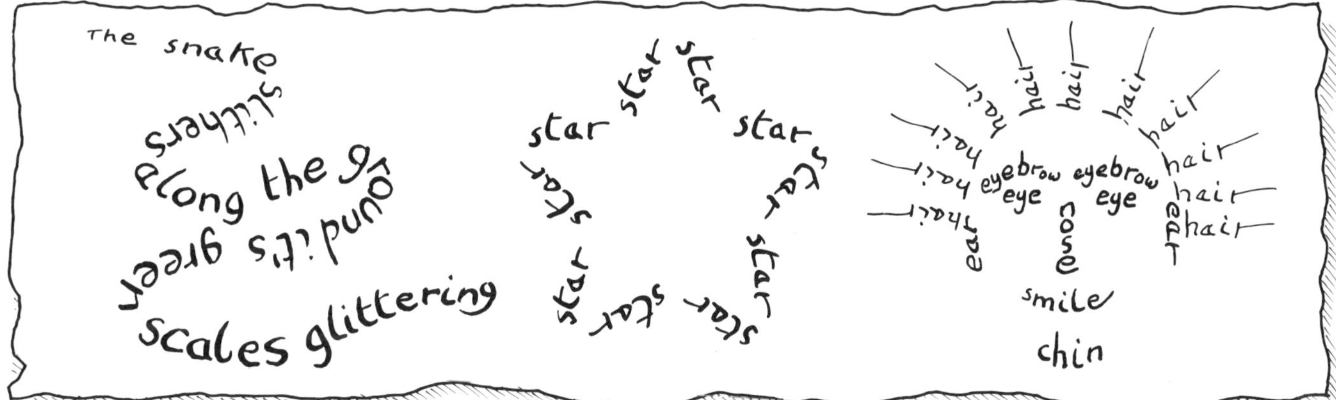

- Write your own space and shape poems using these ideas.

falling downstairs	snow	wind	cloud	bird

Sentences - Ideas Page

Background

Learning to construct sentences is one of the most important skills in learning to write, but we cannot help children by giving them a definition of a sentence. Any definition that is detailed enough to be accurate is bound to be too abstract for most junior children. We can offer tips, techniques and, most important of all, plenty of reading and writing.

Activities

The two most useful tips are given on the activity page. Here are some others:

- Say something, put a full stop, and start again. This is useful for children who tend to make a piece of writing one long sentence.
- Instead of 'and' try a full stop. This is another way to help children who do not write in sentences.
- Ask the children to brainstorm several complete sentences about a subject, then put them together in a piece of writing. Do not worry about the clumsiness that may result – it is helping them to internalise the concept of the sentence.
- Make sure they are confident with the use of capital letters and full stops before going on to exclamation marks and question marks. Since these are most often used in dialogue they can be left until later (see pages 26–31).
- Ask the children to work in pairs, with one child reading a passage aloud slowly (preferably a passage without the complications of dialogue and question marks) while the other listens for the ends of sentences. The two clues are sense, and falling voice intonation. When the child hears this, he or she shouts "FULL STOP!".
- Following on from this game, children who are in doubt about how to punctuate their work should read it aloud.
- Draw attention to sentences in their reading books – 'That's a long sentence', 'Look how many short sentences there are', 'What is this mark called?' (exclamation mark), 'Why is it used here?'
- The difficulty for many children is that they will write as they speak, but nobody speaks in sentences. Reading, reading and more reading is the solution. This helps children to internalise written idioms of language and they will begin to write, not as they speak, but as they read. There will be many benefits in addition to learning to write in sentences.
- The final tip is not to become obsessed with sentences, otherwise you may pass this anxiety on to the children and it will inhibit their writing. If a child seems to be making no progress, leave this aspect of writing, praise what they can do and come back to sentences later.

Follow-up

- Ask the children to show their understanding of the sentences on the activity page by writing five short sentences on simple topics, e.g. my classroom, my favourite television programme.
- Create children's picture books that feature one sentence per page.
- Pass-it-on sentences. One child writes a word on a piece of paper and passes it on, e.g. *Many ...; Many orange ...; Many orange elephants ...* . Sentences should stop by the fourteenth word or earlier. Develop these into stories, one sentence at a time.
- Write alphabet sentences. Use each letter of the alphabet to start a sentence:
  - **A**n awfully big balloon popped.
  - **B**ig balloons are dangerous.
- Use alliterative sentences for each letter of the alphabet:
  - **A**wkward **a**nts **a**re **a**mazing.

Sentences

Sentences

- A sentence is a group of words that makes sense by itself.
- Every sentence begins with a capital letter and ends with a full stop, a question mark or an exclamation mark.

Examples: He caught the ball neatly.
Will you be at the party tonight?
Do not drop that vase!

- Rewrite these five sentences, putting in the capital letters and the full stops, question marks or exclamation marks.

1. i came home early

 ____

2. will you be back before tea

 ____

3. be quiet

 ____

4. i am very fond of painting

 ____

5. the fox went hunting by moonlight

 ____

- Write out the following passage with full stops and capital letters in the correct places.

the teacher was old he had a long white face and long white teeth it was the teeth that worried trevor he had only seen teeth like that once before and that was in a vampire film the teacher told the class to get their books out trevor got his book out then he barked an order that they should work quietly trevor was quiet he decided that this was one teacher he did not want to get into trouble with

Background

- Capital letters are easy both to teach and to learn. The main problem is that children keep forgetting to use them! Young children will write their names without capital letters for a long time after they have been taught about them. This is hardly surprising since capital letters have little practical purpose – they are just historical survivals. In fact, their use continues to dwindle. A decade ago it would have been considered correct to write the seasons with capital letters, e.g. Spring, but now they are usually written without. School subjects (except those derived from proper nouns, e.g. English) are now written without capital letters.
- To start with, the most important uses should be emphasised (see activity page).
- When the children are confident in the use of these they can be introduced to other uses of the capital letter (see grid, page 11).
- A few children may even progress to the thorny problems that exercise adult minds, such as how to write titles (all words begin with capitals except prepositions and conjunctions).
- The golden rule in teaching capital letters is *be patient*. Just keep reminding children to use them.

Activities

- Produce decorated capitals for presenting of pieces of work.
- Animal alphabets. Use the shape of capitals to create images, e.g. C becomes a cat.

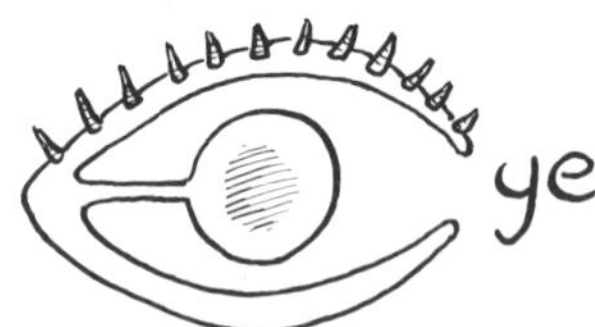

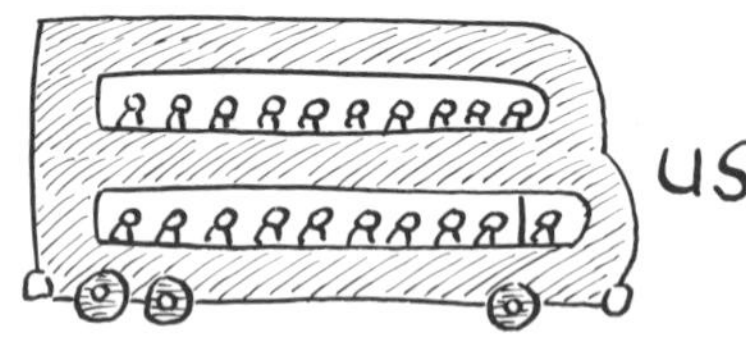

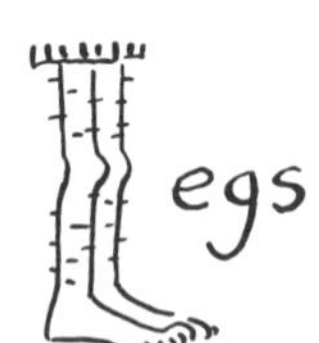

- Children can research the derivation of the following terms:

- Majuscule – capital letters
- Miniscule – small letters
} *terms used by monastic scribes*

- Upper case – capital letters
- Lower case – small letters
} *terms used by printers*

- Swash capitals – ornamental capitals

Follow-up

- The children may find it interesting to investigate why there are capital letters and small letters.
- In the history of most writing systems, only capital letters were used and were usually written on stone, wood or clay. When writing was done in great quantities on papyrus or paper with free flowing ink and a stylus or pen, scribes tended to take short cuts to make writing quicker, often joining letters in a 'cursive' hand.
- Explain this to the children, show them Egyptian, Greek, or other examples of script and let them experiment by writing our own capitals as quickly as possible. Ask them to describe what happens to the shapes.

Capital Letters

Capital Letters

The most important uses of capital letters are:

- to begin sentences, e.g. Once upon a time there was ...
- to begin names of people and places, e.g. Simon, Doncaster.

Here are some more examples and uses:

Use Capital Letters for	Examples	Your Examples
Names of people	Sarah Tony Adams	
Names of places	England San Francisco	
Days, months, special occasions	Monday July	
Brand names	Ford Reebok	
Initials	USA T. J. Hooker	

- Write two more examples of each in the chart.
- Write the capital letters in this passage:

it was only when the bus had started that trevor realised it was a barnsley bus. that meant he could not get off until it stopped at the windmill estate. he would have to wait for a bus back and then wait for a kilnhurst bus. that meant he would be really late for school. mr wilkins would be furious.

Commas: Lists - Ideas Page

Background

This is one of the simplest uses of the comma, the only confusion being whether to put a comma before the 'and' which ends the list. This is partly a matter of personal choice, though modern convention is to leave out the comma. However, for certain types of sentence a comma used before the 'and' can help to clarify meaning, e.g. if the last item needs a phrase to describe it, or if the writer wants to emphasise it in some way, e.g.

> *On my desk there is a diary, a pen, a pair of scissors, and a photograph of my great grandad on his first day at school.*

However, only the most able of children will benefit from having this point explained. For most children the simple guidance on page 13 is enough. Do not make the mistake of telling them never to put a comma before 'and' – they will undoubtedly find several examples to show you the next day!

Activity

Children should complete the first sentence by looking atthe picture and listing the items from left to right. Any children who find this difficult should be given more simple pictures to write about. Most children will be ready to move on to the second picture. This should be treated more flexibly. Ask the children to discuss in pairs what they can see, and then to list those items that interest them. They do not have to list everything.

Follow-up

The order in which list items are placed can have a significant effect on the aesthetic quality of a sentence.

- Encourage the children to experiment with the following:
  - read the lists out loud to find the best word order
  - place humorous or particularly interesting items at the end of a list
  - place long items at the end of a list.
- Encourage the children to write many list sentences. They can:
  - empty their pockets or bags and list the contents
  - list their favourite foods, records, hobbies, etc.
  - list what is around them, e.g. the classroom, the view from the window
  - look at pictures and photographs and list what they see.

  When doing this they should pick out three or four of the most interesting items. Long lists in sentences sound cumbersome.
- Ask the children to write about some of the following, including lists where appropriate:
  - an exciting festival, e.g. Christmas morning
  - a view from my window
  - a description of my friend.

Commas: Lists

Commas

Commas are used to separate items in a list:

On my desk there is a diary, a pen, a pair of scissors and a ruler.

Note: there is not usually a comma before 'and'.

- Look at the pictures and complete the sentences.

On the table there is ...

Through the window I can see ...

- Complete these sentences in the same way, but this time experiment to find the order of words that sounds the best.

On the table there is ...

Through the window I can see ...

Commas: Phrase in Apposition - Ideas Page

Background

- Apart from its simple, clear-cut uses, such as lists (see page 12) and dialogue (see pages 26–31), the comma is the most difficult item of punctuation to teach. It is difficult to go beyond these simple applications without teaching sentence structure, since commas are used to separate certain phrases and clauses. A course on clause analysis is obviously inappropriate to junior age children, so once again we are left with hints and tips.
- Teach the simple uses of the comma described on page 13.
- There is at least one grammatical structure – the phrase in apposition – which can be taught to older and more able junior age children.
- Do not give vague advice such as 'a comma is used to mark a temporary pause in a sentence' or 'a comma shows where you should pause to take a breath'. It can easily be proved that commas do not always indicate pauses by reading a page from any novel.
- A more valuable piece of advice about commas is: if in doubt, leave them out.
- Encourage the children to take note of how commas are used in the books they read.

Activities

- Using commas to include a phrase in apposition is a common way of expanding a sentence and making it more interesting. Page 15 begins with an example, followed by a simple practice exercise. When the children transfer this knowledge to their own writing there may be some clumsy and even grammatically incorrect sentences at first, but for those children who can internalise the concept the benefit is not only a more sophisticated appreciation of commas, but also knowledge of a grammatical technique which will enrich their written descriptions.
- The children could look at their past work and discuss how simple sentences can be made more interesting.
- Add phrases in apposition and rewrite.
- Try out some puzzles on the children. Commas can make the meaning of a sentence much clearer.
- Ask the children to identify the difference between:
  - *Children, who are dirty, must wash.*
  - *Children who are dirty must wash.*
  - *The sphinx, which is in Egypt, is impressive.*
  - *The sphinx which is in Egypt is impressive.*

  In one case the commas act like brackets, the group of words inside them becoming almost an aside. Without commas the words identify something/somebody specific.
- Give the children a simple storyline written in simple sentences:
  - *Guy Fawkes was a traitor.*
  - *He tried to blow up the Houses of Parliament.*
  - *The plot was unsuccessful.*

  Ask the children to elaborate on the story using phrases in apposition:
  - *Guy Fawkes, as history books tell us, was a traitor.*
  - *He tried, unsuccessfully, to blow up the Houses of Parliament.*
  - *The plot, as everyone knows, was discovered.*

Follow-up

- The children could work in pairs to suggest expanding appropriate sentences in each other's writing. This can be incorporated into a collaborative redrafting process that looks at broader aspects of writing.
- Other specific uses of the comma that could be taught to more able children are:
  - marking off an initial conjunction: *'However, when he found out ...'*
  - the question tag: *'It's hot, isn't it?'*
  - marking off the name of the person addressed in direct speech: *'Hello, John.'*

Commas: Phrase in Apposition

Commas

A phrase in apposition is a few words of extra explanation included in a sentence, e.g.

phrase in apposition

Mr Jones, [our next door neighbour], kindly threw my ball back.

The sentence would make sense if the phrase in apposition were removed.

Note: if the phrase comes at the end of a sentence, its final comma is replaced by the full stop.

phrase in apposition

Our next stop was York, [one of the oldest cities in Britain].

- Write the phrases in apposition from the box in the correct sentences.

Rover, [ ], barked at the strangers.

The Mississippi, [ ], flows into the Gulf of Mexico.

We visited Norway, [ ]

Susan, [ ], is five today.

Mr Matthews, [ ], was not amused.

phrases in apposition

a land of mountains and fjords
the longest river in America
the friendly old sheep dog
the head teacher
my youngest sister

- Write five simple sentences of your own. Ask a partner to write in a phrase that makes them more interesting.

Apostrophe: Contractions - *Ideas Page*

Background

- There are two uses for the apostrophe:
  - to show where letters have been omitted in shortened forms
  - to show possession.
- The first is very easy to learn. Many children will be using apostrophes in this way already. However, watch out for these common mistakes:
  - placing the apostrophe where the word space used to be, e.g. had'nt instead of hadn't
  - using shortened forms all the time instead of when appropriate.

Activities

- The first activity can be used for children who are new to this use of the apostrophe, or who are putting it in the wrong place.
- If further reinforcement is needed, adapt the punctuation game on pages 40–41 or use the following exercises:
  - Write out these shortened forms in full:

1.	he's	6.	Ann's
2.	they've	7.	they're
3.	we've	8.	we're
4.	I'm	9.	shouldn't
5.	it's	10.	can't

  - Give the shortened forms of the following:

1.	he will	6.	you had
2.	I am	7.	she has
3.	they have	8.	I would
4.	she is	9.	she had
5.	we are	10.	you will

- The second activity on page 17 is designed to encourage the children to consider when the use of shortened forms is appropriate. They should need little prompting to see that the activity is simply asking them to rewrite the letter with all the shortened forms written in full.

Follow-up

- Make a collection of short texts, e.g. business letters, brochures, extracts from stories containing dialogue, personal letters and postcards, which show how shortened forms are restricted mainly to informal, personal writing and speech.
- Using the activities on page 23, ask the children to write a letter to a friend or relative. Try to make the letter sound as friendly as possible by using shortened forms and personal ways of opening and closing, e.g. instead of 'Yours faithfully', something like 'Lots of love' or 'See you soon'.
- Next they should write a letter to a company or local business to request information for a forthcoming topic (or as part of a simulation as described on page 22). This should be formal in tone, should use full, not shortened forms, and should open and close with the conventional forms of address.
- Look for other examples of shortened forms in stories and letters. Ask the children to bring these to school to create a class display. The different examples can then be used for discussion.
- Ask the children to find out whether people used shortened forms in the past. Ask them to identify which ones were used and which were not, and discuss the reasons for this.

Apostrophes: Contractions

Apostrophes

The apostrophe is used to show where a letter, or letters, have been missed out when words are shortened.

isn't	=	is not	you're	=	you are
can't	=	cannot	don't	=	do not

Note: shortened forms are best used for conversation and informal writing to friends and relatives. Use the long form for all other writing.

- Match the long forms and the short forms below.

- This letter of complaint sounds too friendly.
  How would you improve it?

Dear Sir,

I'm writing to complain about the hole you've dug in the road just outside my house. I can't get my car on to the drive. The workers start very early in the morning and they're always making a noise.

I know the work has to be done, but you didn't write to let me know when it would start. Also, you could have arranged for the workers to lay planks over the hole so that I could get my car across.

Yours faithfully,

Apostrophes: Possession - Ideas Page

Background

The rules for the use of the possessive apostrophe are abstract and confusing. It is not surprising that many adults get it wrong. Here is a real life example of this, which makes the point about the use of the plural possessive apostrophe in a memorable way:

When I was a student, the Students' Union asked a local printing firm to print its membership cards. They arrived some weeks later with the words 'Student's Union' in big gold letters across the top. The President of the Union said jokingly, "These are no good, there's more than one student in my union!" The cards had to be printed again with the apostrophe in the right place, and no doubt, the printer made a loss.

Activities

- Teaching the possessive apostrophe needs great care.
  - Do not try to teach it to children who are not ready.
  - Do not try to teach everything – singular, plural, etc. – at once. Take it one step at a time.
  - Teach it to individuals or small groups as the need arises.
  - Concentrate on getting the simple uses right, e.g. the singular possessive apostrophe used with people's names. Many children will be helped by being restricted to this use until they are fully confident with it.
- The use of the plural possessive apostrophe should only be introduced to children whose knowledge about language is quite advanced.
- The golden rule, 'if in doubt, leave it out', cannot be stressed too often. There is no doubt that a child's work looks worse with a random scattering of apostrophes than with none at all.
- Plural possession is very complex and attempting to teach it to junior age children will probably do more harm than good. However, for the minority of pupils who are ready to be taught it, the rule is included in the template at the top of the activity page.
- The 'Whose is It?' game on page 20 is a practical and enjoyable way of learning about the use of the plural possessive apostrophe.

Answers

1. The budgie's beak (the beak of the budgie).
2. Brian's plan (the plan of Brian).
3. Granny's pension book (the pension book of Granny).
4. Dracula's teeth (the teeth of Dracula).
5. Greta's breath (the breath of Greta).

Follow-up

- There is an alarming number of examples of the apostrophe being used wrongly by adults. This can most often be seen in business signs, on vehicles and shops. Ask the children to do some research as they are walking around their local community, and to write down the number of incorrect examples they can find. Hopefully, this will reinforce their own pride in using the apostrophe correctly.
- Help the children to create their own tests from examples they have found, to see how much their classmates (and their teachers) know.

Apostrophes: Possession

Apostrophes

The apostrophe is a sign (') used to show possession (belonging to). Make sure the apostrophe goes in the right place.

Add ' before the s for one, e.g. Brian's friend (The friend of Brian).

Add ' after the s for more than one, e.g. The Students' Union (The Union of the Students).

If a word ends in s already, just add the apostrophe, e.g. John Keats' poems (The poems of John Keats).

● Write two sentences about these pictures.

The dog ate a biscuit.

● Add apostrophes in the correct places in these sentences.

1. The gobstopper stuck in the budgies beak.
2. Brians plan went wrong.
3. The tea spilled over Grannys pension book.
4. Draculas teeth glinted in the moonlight.
5. Gretas breath came in short, nervous gasps.

Whose is It? - Ideas Page

Background

The use of the possessive apostrophe is potentially one of the most confusing points of punctuation that children need to learn. The 'Whose is It?' card game is a way to reinforce the basic principles taught on page 18 in an enjoyable way.

Activity

STAGE ONE

- On the activity page are six characters and six objects. These should be cut out and, if possible, mounted on card and laminated so that they become a permanent resource. The children play in pairs. One child has the characters and the other the objects. They shuffle their cards, and take it in turn to deal to each other, so that each child finally has three pairs of cards. Each child then turns the cards over to see what the combinations are. Some of them may be quite amusing! They then write a phrase about each pair using the correct punctuation. Tell them what sort of phrase you want, i.e.

  [name]'s [*object*], e.g. the vicar's Bible

  the [*object*] is [name]'s, e.g. the Bible is the vicar's

  Before moving on to Stage Two, ensure that the children are fully confident with these patterns. Further practise will be more fun if a number of similar sheets are devised. These can then be used for Stage Two.

STAGE TWO

Stage Two offers practice in some of the more complex uses of the possessive apostrophe.

- Use an extended set of cards with at least twelve extra object cards. When dealing, each child should now be given one person card and three object cards. The phrase will now have to include three nouns, the first two separated by a comma, e.g.
  - The Bible, CD player and motorbike are the vicar's.
  - The vicar's Bible, CD player and motorbike.

- Photocopy the activity sheet three times and create groups of people, e.g. the 'Elaine' cards are now 'girls'. Remind the children that groups take the plural possessive – **s'**. Now they are ready to play. Cards are dealt so that each child has one or more groups of people, each group matched with one object card to begin with, and two or three at a later stage.

Well structured practice with these cards can do a great deal to remove confusion about singular and plural possessive apostrophes.

Follow-up

Many of the combinations thrown up in the game are amusing, interesting or stimulating to the imagination. The children could take some of the combinations they have found most interesting and write a story around them. The story will provide opportunities to practise the use of the possessive apostrophe in context.

Whose is It?

Elaine
bikini
Dr Frankenstein
the vicar
Bible
pet monster
Mr Jenkinson
car phone
Rover
Trevor
computer game
bone

Letters - Ideas Page

Background

Writing letters is not as simple as it looks. As well as punctuation, there are a great many conventions of setting out to be considered, and social conventions. For example, a secretary would set out an address on a word processor differently to the way it would be written by hand at home. An old person would use different conventions from a young person.

Activities

- The aim of the first activity on page 23 is to emphasise that there is no one correct way to write addresses, but that there is a range of styles. The tendency now is towards simple form. The 'open punctuation' of the third example is a widely used convention of office practice and is spreading to personal letters. However, it is still worthwhile for the children to learn how to punctuate addresses traditionally, as in the first example.
- The second activity can be used as a guide for the children's own letter writing. Ask them to study this carefully in pairs by looking for:
  - the way it is set out – spaces, etc.
  - where capital letters are used
  - where punctuation is used.
- Ask the children to discuss the setting out activity on the sheet, then bring their discussions together by pointing out that the example ends with 'Yours sincerely'. Note 'Yours' always has a capital letter and 'faithfully' or 'sincerely' do not. If children begin letters with 'Dear Sir' or 'Dear Madam', they should end it 'Yours faithfully'. This is more formal than 'Yours sincerely' which they would use if they began with someone's name. There are many friendlier ways to end a personal letter – 'With love', 'Best wishes', etc. Letter writing is a good way to show the children how written style changes for audience and purpose.
- The children should work on the abbreviations in pairs and try to write them out in full. Ask them what the full stop is there for (it signals an abbreviation).
- Ask the children to write some fun letters to fictional characters, e.g. what would Little Red Riding Hood write to her Grandma? Ask the children to choose an ending for this letter.

Follow-up

- In the early days of the postal system there were no standard conventions for postal addresses and most houses were not numbered. People would address their letters as best as they could, writing down whatever might be helpful, e.g.

  Mr J. Smith, third house along from the 'Alma' Inn, at the end of the new road in Coningsburgh.

  Ask the children to write their own address in this way.
- It is important to ensure that the children have opportunities to write letters for real purposes as part of their writing programme, e.g.:
  - letters to friends
  - letters to relatives requesting information for a topic
  - letters that might have been written by characters in a book they are reading.
- Older and more able children might be ready to study business letters. The best way to do this is to look at some real examples and use them as models. They could then:
  - write letters as part of a classroom simulation, e.g. a letter of protest about an environmental issue
  - write to authors about their books, or to businesses requesting information for a topic.
- Finally, a worthwhile fun activity is to take apart an envelope very carefully and to use it as a template for the children to make their own.

Letters

Here are three ways you might see an address written.

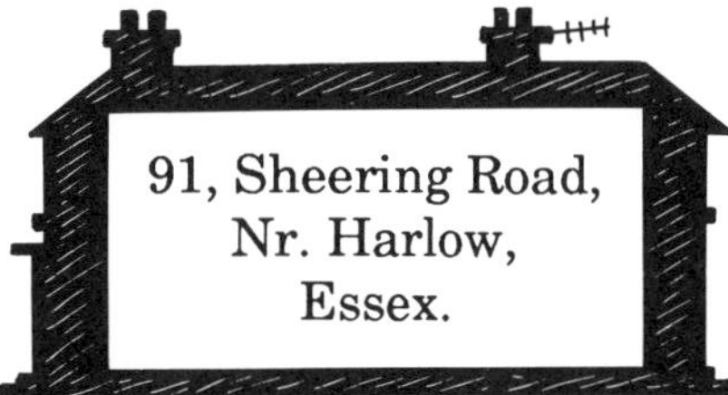

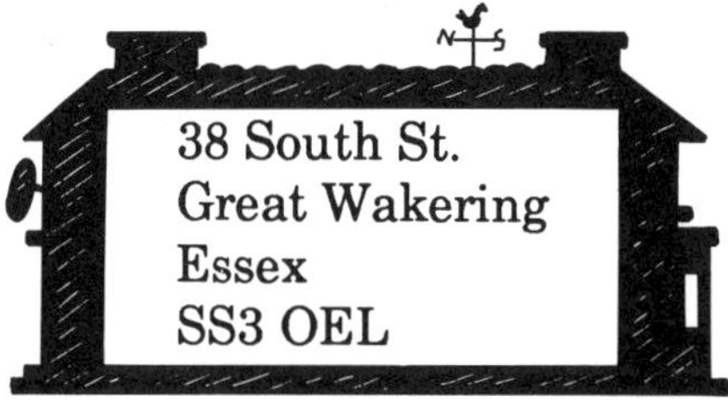

- What are the differences?
- Which do you think is the most old fashioned? Which is the most modern?
- Which look as though they are official letters and which look as though they are personal letters?

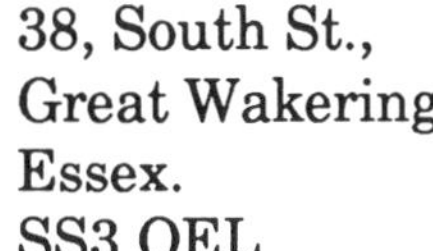

Letters

There are other important points of punctuation and setting out to learn. Use this pattern to help you.

38, South St.,
Great Wakering,
Essex.
SS3 OEL

14th June

Dear Judith,

Thank you very much for looking after the cat while we were away. She's certainly looking well. I hope she didn't upset your budgie.

Let me know how much I owe you for the repairs to the curtains and the carpet cleaning.

Yours sincerely,

- How many other ways are there to end letters? Find out about the rules for their use.

NOW Addresses often use abbreviations. What do these abbreviations stand for?

CRESC.	AVE.	SQ.	RD.
ST.	BLDGS.	PL.	GDNS.
BLVD.			

Horror Letters - Ideas Page

Background

Page 22 recommends a range of real audiences for letter writing. However, these are few and easily exhausted. Another problem is that replies take time and can be uncertain. For these reasons, letter writing simulations are the ideal way to provide day-to-day practice.

Activity

- Ask the children to choose a horror character from the activity page. Their address can be seen in the picture. They then have to think of a suitable reason for writing and compose a correctly punctuated and set out letter, referring to the example on page 23 if necessary. Added spice can be given to the simulation by saying that the horror characters get very angry if they receive incorrect letters. The children could suggest the outcome of this.

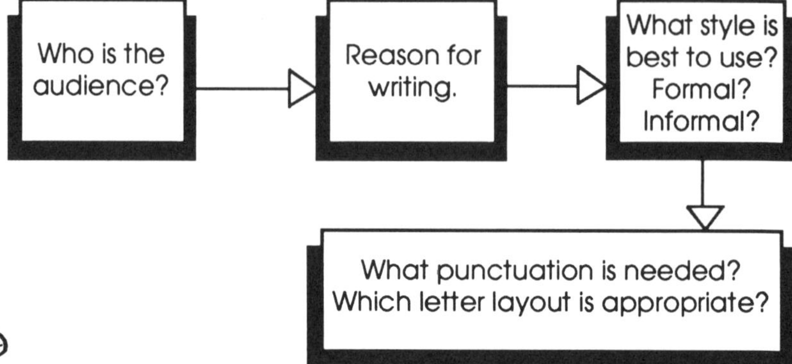

- When letters have been written, ask the children to exchange them with a partner and write replies.

Follow-up

- The idea can be developed by providing complete writing simulations for use with small groups of children. For example, the children could write to Dracula for permission to visit his castle. Dracula could reply, enclosing a 'free pardon', i.e. a document granting five days' access to the castle. The children could then write a letter describing a night spent in Castle Dracula. The simulation could be extended to include other types of writing, e.g. a story or a newspaper report.
- Novels written as a series of letters were very popular in the eighteenth century and the idea could be used to practise letter writing. A good way to do it would be to set up a simulation similar to the one described above. Tell the children what the stages of the simulation are, e.g.

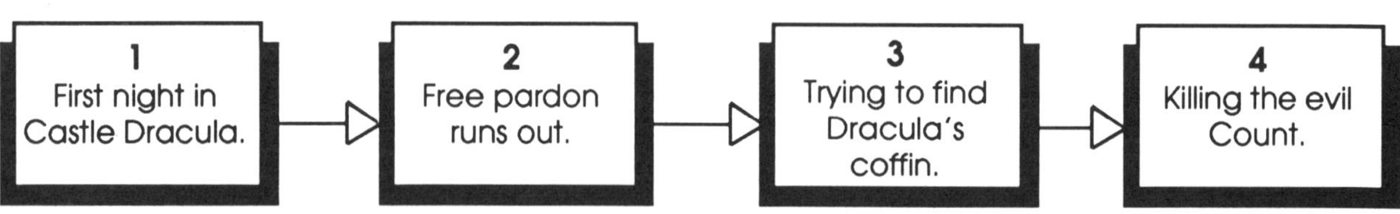

- The letters produced in the simulation could be put together and edited to tell the story. The children could also look at Bram Stoker's original text which is similar as it is written in journal form. Another idea would be to take an Adrian Mole situation, but write letters instead of diary entries.
- Letter writing can be included in a wide range of cross-curricular topics, such as seeking information, e.g. writing to businesses or relatives, or in a simulation where children playing a role write letters to each other.

Horror Letters

Write a letter to one of the characters on this sheet. Do not forget to set it out and punctuate it correctly.

NOW

- Swap your letters with a partner and write a reply.

Dialogue: 'Knock, Knock' Jokes - Ideas Page

Background

- The first step in teaching the punctuation of speech is to ask the children to place inverted commas before and after the words actually spoken. Many children pick this up from their own reading or from parents. They should not be held back by going through the process described below, but could go straight on to the activity on page 29.
- Different teachers and text books use different terms, e.g. '66 and 99', 'speech marks', 'conversation marks', 'inverted commas' or 'quotation marks'. You should choose a terminology which suits the age and ability of your children, but as soon as possible, introduce the term 'inverted commas'. This term is preferable because it covers all the possible uses, from speech to quotations.

Activities

Children who are having difficulty or who have never been taught should be taught in simple stages.

- Begin by reading suitable books containing simple dialogue. Point out the inverted commas, and ask why they are there.
- Next, give them a page from the same book from which the inverted commas have been removed. Ask them to put them in.
- Children who have difficulty doing this are usually uncertain which words are actually spoken. They can be helped by reading dialogue passages in pairs. One child is the narrator, the other (the child who is having difficulty) reads out the words actually spoken. The more realistically the child can do this, the more the dialogue will stand out from the narrated text.
- Understanding should then be checked by repeating the punctuation exercise. Do not worry if the child still does not understand. Leave it for now and move on to some other aspect of language. Sometimes the concept needs time to be absorbed.
- See also page 32, which shows how cartoons can be used as another way to teach the same point.
- When the children have grasped the basic idea of inverted commas before and after speech, 'Knock, Knock' jokes can be used as an enjoyable way to reinforce the learning, and to take some simple steps forward in:
  - line layout, the idea of a new line for a new speaker
  - other punctuation that is used in speech
  - speech marks inside speech marks.

Follow-up

- Many other jokes are based on dialogue. Ask children to work in pairs or small groups to write out and punctuate these jokes.
  - "What did the salad say when it knocked on the door?"
    "Lettuce in!"
  - "When is the only time a rope is clever?"
    "When it's taut!"
- Ask children to experiment by writing short passages of conversation using similar patterns to the jokes.
- Encourage them to use conversation in their stories and to punctuate it with inverted commas.
- Encourage children to write short play scripts without inverted commas, then to turn them into stories by adding description. The dialogue will then need to be made clear by adding inverted commas. This is a good way of helping them to see the need for inverted commas (see page 42).

'Knock, Knock' Jokes

Dialogue

- Speech marks, or inverted commas, are used before and after the words which are actually spoken.
- A new line is used every time the speaker changes. This makes it clearer for the reader.

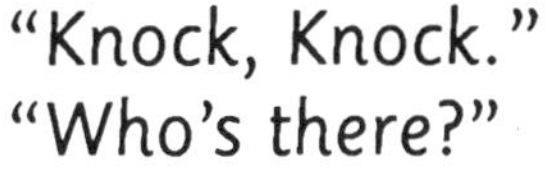

"Knock, Knock."
"Who's there?"
"__________."
"__________ who?"
"______________________."

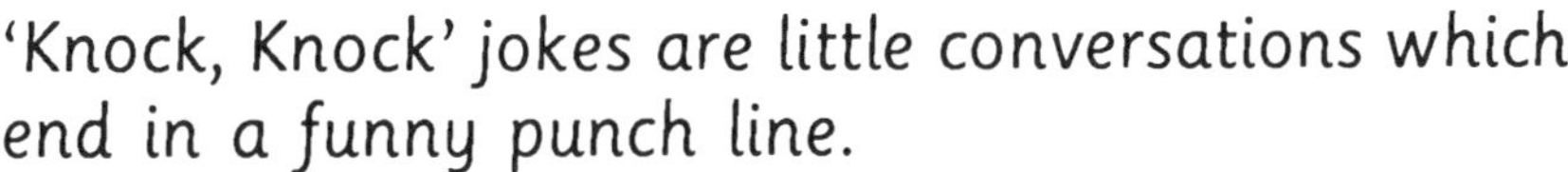

'Knock, Knock' jokes are little conversations which end in a funny punch line.

- Punctuate these 'Knock, Knock' jokes:

- How many more 'Knock, Knock' jokes do you know? Take it in turns to tell them to each other, write them down and punctuate them.

Dialogue: Two Simple Patterns - Ideas Page

Background

- Dealing with dialogue is undoubtedly the greatest challenge in learning about punctuation. In a line of dialogue the punctuation comes thick and fast – the children have a great deal to remember in just a few words of text.
- This activity page covers two of the most common dialogue patterns, and so these exercises are particularly important.

Activity

- Begin by helping the children to look carefully at the two dialogue patterns on the activity page. They can do this in pairs. Ask the children to use a red pen to mark every item of punctuation and every capital letter, and then to punctuate the ten sentences.
- Note that the children are prompted to use an exclamation mark or a question mark in place of the full stop or comma. Question marks are often forgotten, yet about a third of an average conversation will be made up of questions. Group the children in threes to explore this – two to talk, one to count the questions. Each child should have a turn at listening.
- Exclamation marks are the most difficult to teach because their use is often a matter of stylistic choice. Encourage the children to use them when a speaker is shouting or surprised. They could try listening for these in the way described above.

Follow-up

- **The Punctuation Chorus Game.** This game is great fun and is a valuable way of increasing children's awareness of all the items of punctuation that are used in dialogue.
  - children work in groups of five
  - child one is the reader
  - child two is the inverted commas
  - child three is a full stop
  - child four is a comma
  - child five takes on anything else (e.g. apostrophes, exclamation marks, question marks)
  - children two to five make up a humorous noise to represent their punctuation, e.g. a popping noise for a full stop, a scream for an exclamation mark
  - child one then reads a line of dialogue (slowly) and the other pupils make their punctuation noises in the correct places.

  This technique can be used for short sentences of dialogue, dialogue exercises and even whole passages of dialogue. Have fun!

- Encourage the children to punctuate the dialogue in their stories. Note that this is most effective if it is done as part of the redrafting process. When they first start to punctuate dialogue there will be so much to remember that the flow of creativity could be impeded. The children should be encouraged to write the story down, then to go back, remind themselves of these patterns and carefully to punctuate the dialogue. Of course, they should be working towards the ability to punctuate as they go along.
- Teaching the punctuation of dialogue should be an integrated process. The children should look at how dialogue is punctuated in the books they read, study it in detail using the ideas in these pages and use it in writing their own stories.

Answers

1. "You look like a ghost," said Sarah.
2. The ghost replied, "That's because I am a ghost."
3. Sarah screamed at the top of her voice, "A ghost!"
4. "You're deafening me!" exclaimed the ghost.
5. "Sorry," said Sarah.
6. "Are you really a ghost?" asked Sarah, after a moment.
7. The ghost sighed, "What do you think?"
8. Sarah said, "I can see through you."
9. "What do you mean?" asked the ghost.
10. "I can see through the trick you're playing!" laughed Sarah.

Dialogue: Two Simple Patterns

Dialogue

Here are two common dialogue patterns:

"You shelter in that old house," said Sarah.

The ghost whispered, "Someone's coming."

Note: you could use ! or ? instead of . or , .

- Punctuate these sentences of dialogue.

1. you look like a ghost said sarah
2. the ghost replied thats because i am a ghost
3. sarah screamed at the top of her voice a ghost
4. youre deafening me exclaimed the ghost
5. sorry said sarah
6. are you really a ghost asked sarah after a moment
7. the ghost sighed what do you think
8. sarah said I can see through you
9. what do you mean asked the ghost
10. i can see through the trick youre playing laughed sarah

- Turn the sentences into a story. Add description and explain more about how and why the trick was played on Sarah.

Dialogue: Setting It Out - Ideas Page

Background

- This activity page aims to teach the children the final stages in the punctuation of dialogue, where everything comes together: the two simple punctuation patterns covered on page 28, plus the correct setting out.

Activities

- Before the children tackle the activity page, it might be worth spending some time teaching the third common pattern for dialogue exemplified in the third line of the extract:

  "I don't know," replied Tony, "it's pitch dark and I can't see my watch."

- A template for this pattern should be made and children encouraged to find examples in their reading books and to try it in their own writing. Note that the following variation is also correct:

  "I don't know." replied Tony. "It's pitch dark and I can't see my watch."

  The full stop creates a greater separation between the two sections of speech. These fine distinctions are too sophisticated for the vast majority of junior children and so the first of the two patterns should be taught. However, it may be worth discussing the second pattern since the children will undoubtedly come across it in their reading.
- Setting out dialogue as a new paragraph for each change of speaker (the term paragraph is used for convenience – they are not paragraphs in the proper sense of the word) is easy enough in its simple form (see page 26) and can be reinforced by writing play scripts. The real challenge is integrating the phrases of description. The dialogue in the extract has been written to exemplify some of the common patterns in children's books.
- The next step is for the children to work in pairs to punctuate and set out the passage of dialogue. While doing this, the children should use the extract and refer to examples in their reading books.
- The children can try to consolidate what they have learned by writing a short dialogue on a suggested title, e.g.
  - The argument
  - Hurry up, it's time for school
  - Trouble with parents

  Note that these are exercises. The children should concentrate on punctuation and layout, rather than an exciting storyline or realistic dialogue.

Follow-up

- Alongside these exercises, the children should also study dialogue itself so that they can use their punctuation skills effectively
  This can be done by:
  - listening to and discussing dialogue in favourite soap operas, at home, in the playground, etc.
  - writing short play scripts, which allow emphasis to be placed on realism without worrying about punctuation
  - brainstorming synonyms for 'said', so that dialogue in stories can be written more effectively. Discuss words such as 'replied', 'enquired', 'pleaded' and 'exclaimed' with the children and look at what they bring to the dialogue. Try adding a descriptive phrase which tells the reader something of the mood, feelings or tone of voice of the speaker, e.g. "I'm fed up," said Sarah sulkily.
- Turning a story into a play / Turning a play into a story } are useful ways of creating dialogue exercises.

Dialogue: Setting It Out

Dialogue

Look at this extract from a children's story. After a line of description, there are several lines of dialogue:

> Stephen and Tony huddled in the dark cave wishing that the rain would stop.
>
> "What time is it?" asked Stephen.
>
> "I don't know," replied Tony, "it's pitch dark and I can't see my watch."
>
> "Use the torch. It's over there somewhere."
>
> Tony groped around in the darkness. "It's no good. I can't find it and I've looked everywhere. Are you sure you haven't got it?"
>
> "Certain."
>
> "Wait a minute. What's this!"
>
> "That's not it – it's my foot, you fool!"

Note: there is a new paragraph for each change of speaker.

- Take turns to read passage A aloud to each other. The lines of dialogue are not written on separate lines. Can you read it aloud without making any mistakes?

- Punctuate it and set it out in paragraphs like the example above.

A

Mr Jones looked at the Porsche longingly. He liked its shape, and its bright red paintwork, but he did not like the price tag on the windscreen. The salesman moved in for the kill.
This is the car for you sir said the salesman smoothly.
Only one owner, perfect condition, and very easy on petrol.
I don't know, said Mr Jones doubtfully. It's not quite what I had in mind. I wouldn't touch this foreign rubbish if I were you sir answered the salesman quickly. They look good, but they're always letting you down, most unreliable. Still, muttered Mr Jones, this is a bit expensive isn't it? One year's guarantee, sir. Buy one of the others, you'll pay extra in repairs and service. This little beauty will run for years, no danger.

- Write a short conversation using all you have learned about the punctuation and paragraphing of speech.

Cartoon Crazy - Ideas Page

Background

Comic strips can be used in several ways to teach aspects of punctuation. They offer an ideal opportuntiy to explore techniques of combining narrative and dialogue.

Activities

The exercise on the activity page requires a sound knowledge of the basic conventions of dialogue and can be used to reinforce skills already acquired. As a follow-up it would be interesting to turn the idea around and ask children to turn one of their stories into a comic strip.

Follow-up

- Some children experience confusion about exactly where to place inverted commas. Speech bubbles can be used to explain this point as follows:

- Comic strips can be used to motivate the children. Punctuation is not the most exciting subject in the world, but if they are set work which is based on their favourite comics, they are likely to be highly motivated.
- Give the children a cartoon strip with the words blanked out. This increases their creative involvement. They can then go through the processes described on the activity page.
- Note: one of the conventions of speech bubbles is to write all the text in capital letters. Encourage the children to use the usual mixture of capitals and lower case. For younger or less able children it would be wise to rewrite any examples to avoid confusion.

- The children might find it easier to write the dialogue on large wall displays of cartoons rather than on small ones. This can develop into an art project looking at how modern artists, e.g. Lichtenstein, use the cartoon style in their work, or into a history project. Consider the Bayeux tapestry as the most famous cartoon strip in history. Create a version in the classroom, research the Battle of Hastings and its causes. Discuss what the characters might be saying to one another about the reasons for the battle and about the events around them.

Cartoon Crazy

Rewrite this cartoon as a story.

- Describe what you see in the picture.
- Write the contents of the speech bubbles in inverted commas.
- Do not forget the other punctuation.
- Write dialogue with different 'said' phrases.
- The first box has been done for you.

During the six o'clock news there was an important newsflash. The newsreader said, "Reports are coming in of attacks all over the city. Severe damage has been caused to many buildings and vehicles."

____

____

____

____

____

____

Continue on the back ...

? or ! - Ideas Page

Background

- It is difficult enough to teach children to use full stops, but teaching them to remember question marks and exclamation marks is even more difficult!
- Of the two, question marks are the easier to use – though occasionally there are problems in indentifying a question.
- The use of exclamation marks is harder to explain. Exclamations are phrases or sentences that express something emphatically. This is shown in speech by intonation and in writing by an exclamation mark. However, this definition will be of little help to the children, so the simpler definition on the activity page is recommended instead. This should be combined with a study of the way exclamation marks are used in the books they read.

Activity

The speech bubbles activity is an enjoyable way for the children to practise the use of question and exclamation marks. The speech bubble can be filled in many different ways and it really does not matter what the children write as long as they punctuate it correctly. They should work in pairs, taking turns to fill in each speech bubble, and then attempt the follow-up activity. When they have done this they may enjoy taking one of the scenes they have drawn and turning it into a longer strip cartoon of their own. Again, the emphasis should be on correctly punctuating the speech bubbles.

Follow-up

- Working in pairs, the children could read aloud selected passages of dialogue from stories or plays, with special emphasis on intonation. This could be turned into a game. One child reads aloud while the other listens carefully for exclamations or questions. When they hear one they shout out 'Question!' or 'Exclamation!'. The reader then says whether this is correct or incorrect.
- After this, the children could write their own short dialogues in stories or plays concentrating on using punctuation, particularly exclamation marks and question marks, to help the reader. The passages should then be tested by reading them aloud.
- Since exclamation marks and question marks are particularly easy to forget, it would be useful to make a poster based on the activity sheet, using similar cartoons.
- Encourage the children to read their work aloud as part of the drafting process. This will help them to identify a wide range of problems as well as practise the need for question marks and exclamation marks.
- The use of exclamation marks can be taught using onomatopoeic words. Create sound words:

  Draw and colour these in cartoon form, emphasising the exclamation marks. Display these and write poems using only such onomatopoeic words.
- Another fun activity is to write poems using only questions:
  - where is he?
  - who?
  - what are you saying?

  Investigate how long poems can become when they are passed around the class.

? or !

? or !

It is very easy to forget to use a question mark or exclamation mark.

A question mark is used after a question, e.g. "What time is it?".

An exclamation mark is used to show surprise, delight or when someone shouts out, e.g. "How strange!", "What a nice day!", "Help!".

- Look at the pictures and guess what each character is saying. Fill in the speech bubbles. Use question marks or exclamation marks at the end of each speech.

- Sketch your own scenes. Ask a partner to fill in the speech bubbles.

Paragraphs - Ideas Page

Background

This book deals with punctuation in its broadest sense, which includes the use of space to organise text and make it easier to read. The most important example of this is the space between words (see page 6). We take this for granted and it only occasionally causes problems (e.g. on to, or onto?). The two main challenges for children are paragraphing and setting out dialogue (see page 30).

Activities

- The concept of a paragraph, like the concept of a sentence, is acquired gradually through use. It is very difficult to give a useful definition of a paragraph. The activity page includes an example for the children to study, because one of the best ways to learn about paragraphing is to become familiar with their appearance. Two points in the first box concentrate on how paragraphs should look. Some children can be helped by being asked to draw a faint second margin to use for paragraph beginnings. The point about not leaving a blank line between paragraphs is based on current conventions.
- The appearance of paragraphs is fairly easy to grasp, but it is much more difficult to know when to begin a new paragraph. The first box contains a number of guidelines which are at least a starting point for discussion. The point can be further explored by studying paragraphing in children's reading books.
- Paragraphing of writing can be greatly helped by careful planning, perhaps using flow diagrams.
- The exercise in studying reading books recognises that the best way to learn about most aspects of language is to study good examples in use.
- In the final exercise, the titles are followed by suggestions about the number of paragraphs which could be used. This technique works for short pieces of about one page in length and can help to give children a sense of the shape and structure of paragraphs. When they have internalised this, they will start new paragraphs automatically, or after a moment's consideration. The advantage of using a word processor is obvious here, since children can experiment with the paragraphing of a piece.
- If a word processor is not available, cut up the paragraphs in a story and ask the children to sequence them in the light of the five rules given in the first box.
- Give the children passages which have not been paragraphed. Ask them if they are easy to read and understand and then compare their responses.

Follow-up

- Do not introduce paragraphs too soon. The children should be reasonably confident about writing in sentences and the basic punctuation of dialogue before the subject is introduced.
- Beware of the tendency to make each sentence a paragraph. It is possible for a paragraph to be one sentence long, but only as a contrast to longer paragraphs (or in dialogue).
- Encourage children to write in paragraphs. Even if they divide up their text clumsily at first and start paragraphs in the wrong places, they have at least made a start on which to build.

- A useful visual representation of paragraphing is of a series of supports holding up a bridge.

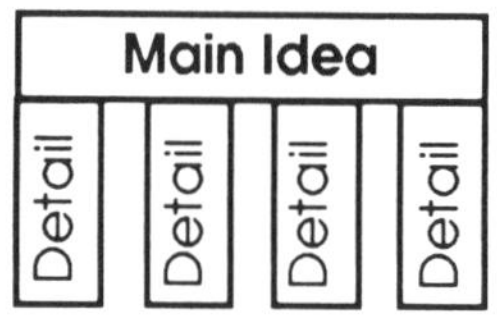

Paragraph 1

Main Idea

Detail Detail Detail Detail

Paragraph 2

- Cut up strips of paper for various groups. Write a 'main idea' sentence (e.g. 'I went on holiday to the mountains last year.') on one strip and give it to each group. Each group has to write 'detail' sentences about the main idea on their strips, e.g. 'The sun shone all week.', 'I went sailing on a lake.'. All the strips are then pasted in sensible order showing how a paragraph has a sentence followed by relevant detail.

Paragraphs

Paragraphs

A paragraph is a group of sentences dealing with one part of a main topic.

- The first line of each paragraph is indented. Indent your own paragraphs about two centimetres from the margin.
- Do not leave a whole blank line between paragraphs.
- Begin a new paragraph for:

1.	A new scene or place	e.g.	When they went outside ...
2.	A new time	e.g.	Next morning ...
3.	A new character	e.g.	A mysterious stranger entered
4.	A change of speaker	e.g.	In speech
5.	A change of subject	e.g.	In a non-fictional piece of writing

- Read the passage below which contains three paragraphs.

It was a sunny day and the beach was very crowded. The sand was hot and it made the boy's feet hurt as he walked along. He was trying to find a good place to build a sandcastle.

The boy turned towards the sea and saw a little girl splashing about in the water, bobbing up and down. At first he thought the water was too deep and she couldn't swim, but then he noticed that she was laughing. He decided to go for a swim to cool off, even though the sea was almost as crowded as the beach.

Later that day some clouds covered the sun and the sand began to cool. The boy built a sandcastle with a moat which he filled with water. Slowly the people began to go home and soon the boy was alone on the beach with his bucket and spade.

Does the passage follow the rules?

- Work in pairs and look carefully at your reading book. Examine how the story has been divided up into paragraphs. Why did the writer decide to start each new paragraph? Use the list of reasons above to help you.

- Write in paragraphs on one of the following titles:

My best friend and my worst enemy (two paragraphs).

Three things I dislike (three paragraphs).

Four of my favourite possessions (four paragraphs).

Shoebox Theatre - Ideas Bank

Background

The punctuation and setting out of direct speech is one of the most complex punctuation tasks children ever have to undertake. The Shoebox Theatre provides an enjoyable way for the children to practise the skills covered on pages 26–31.

Activity

- The first step is for the children, working in pairs or threes, to prepare their theatre. A shoebox, cereal packet, or similar cardboard box is prepared as follows:

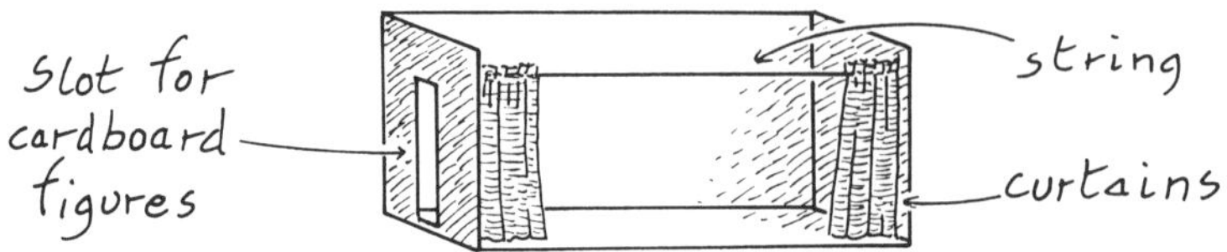

- This can be further embellished by the addition of curtains, electric lights, and backdrops. An easy and effective way to produce realistic backdrops is to cut pictures out of magazines.
- The next step is to cut out and colour the figures on the activity page and mount them on card. They should then be glued or stapled on to strips of stiff card so that they can be controlled from the side.

- The children then make up a short play involving the characters on the sheet. These are fairy story characters and will suit a wide range of fairy stories and folk tales. If the children wish to make up a play on a different subject they can draw their own figures or cut figures out of magazines. An amusing comedy could be performed using figures cut out of a comic.
- The children should improvise their play to begin with. Then, when they are happy with the lines, they should write them down. This simple format is recommended:

Margin

Name of character → BILL | Where's my dog? ← dialogue

- Groups of children then take it in turns to perform their play to other groups.
- The script writing activity reinforces the idea of a new line for each new speaker. This can be transferred into fiction writing by asking the children to write the story version of their play, keeping as much of the dialogue as possible, but adding description.

Follow-up

Final drafts of the play script and story versions could be illustrated with pictures from the activity page and displayed side by side.

Shoebox Theatre

Punctuation Game - Ideas Page

Background

This game is simply a fun way to give the children a punctuation exercise. Children who find punctuation difficult can play the game in pairs.

Activity

- Each box should be cut out and mounted on a piece of card. Additional cards can be designed to suit particular needs. The examples are general in scope and are aimed at an average middle junior class. Other cards could focus on one area only, e.g. the apostrophe, or be made easier or more difficult to suit a different age or ability range. Note that the examples often require more than one item of punctuation. You may decide to limit this to one piece of missing punctuation per card – this depends on the age and ability of your children.
- It may be helpful to have the answers written on the back of the cards. This is particularly useful with younger and less able children, as the game may be frequently held up while they seek arbitration from the teacher. Cheating is unlikely to take place because of the 'game' element – each child effectively monitoring the other. It may be worth spending some time preparing an extended bank of cards covering all aspects of punctuation for all the ability levels in your class. These could be pasted on to stiff card and laminated. The resource will amply repay the time spent in preparing it.
- The cards are shuffled and placed face up (so that the answers on the reverse cannot be seen) in a pile in the middle of the table. The children take turns to select a card. They then have to point out to their partner where the punctuation should go (or write it down). The answer can be checked by turning the card over. If the children are correct they keep the card. If they are wrong the card is placed at the bottom of the pile. The game ends when all the cards are used. The winner is the child with most cards.

Answers

didn't
My budgie can talk.
I'm tired.
What did you say?
isn't
"Have a nice day," she said.
Sharon went to London.
"Help!" he shouted.
"Who's there?" gasped Sue.
It is raining today.
Today is Wednesday.
don't
It is ten miles to York.
couldn't
"Oh no!" he exclaimed.
aren't
Alison's coat
That pen is Susan's.
wouldn't
"I'm hungry!" he exclaimed.
"Where is it?" she asked.
ten o'clock
Tony said, "That's mine."
mustn't
Tony's dog
"How old are you?" he asked.
She's sixteen next Monday.
New York is in America.

Follow-up

- Discuss the punctuation issues on the cards.
- When the game is over and all the cards have been punctuated, turn them over so that the fully punctuated answers can be seen, then place them in a heap in the middle of the table, mix them up, and ask each child to take turns to select four cards without looking. Ask the children to improvise an oral story which includes the words on the cards. This is great fun and very entertaining, and children are surprisingly adept at it.
- When the oral storytelling is over, ask the children to produce a written version of their story, keeping their four cards in front of them. The idea behind the game is to take the out-of-context exercise and put it back into the context of a piece of writing.

Punctuation Game

didnt	oh no he exclaimed
my budgie can talk	arent
Im tired	alisons coat
what did you say	that pen is susans
isnt	wouldnt
have a nice day she said	Im hungry he exclaimed
sharon went to london	where is it she asked
help he shouted	ten o clock
whos there gasped sue	tony said thats mine
it is raining today	mustnt
today is wednesday	tonys dog
dont	how old are you he asked
it is ten miles to york	shes sixteen next monday
couldnt	new york is in america

Punctuation Cards - Ideas Page

Background

It is not easy to make punctuation fun, but that is what this activity tries to do. Basically, the game is just a punctuation exercise, but it has been designed to encourage collaboration and an element of competition in a way that makes such an exercise a profitable learning experience.

Activity

- The passage for punctuation should be carefully chosen:
  - to emphasise a particular point
  - to suit the age and ability of the children.

  The example on the activity page has been chosen for the top junior age range. One copy of the passage is needed for each group of three or four children.
- The next step is to prepare the punctuation cards. Ideally there should be one card for each piece of punctuation in the passage. This is fairly easy to arrange for simple passages, but rather more difficult for complex passages where punctuation can occasionally be a matter of personal preference. The cards will need to be photocopied twice to provide enough punctuation for the passage. It is worth considering making a permanent set of punctuation cards of a larger (credit-card) size made of cardboard, and possibly laminated.
- Each group needs a passage to punctuate and a set of punctuation cards. Each player needs a pen or pencil of a different colour.
- The punctuation cards are shuffled and dealt out among the children in the group. Before play can begin, the children should read the passage to get some idea of the punctuation that will be needed. Cards are held face down to play. Player one selects a card from the top of his or her pack and places it face up in the centre of the table. He or she then has to find a place in the passage where the punctuation shown on the card is needed and mark it in his or her own colour. The next player then takes a turn. If a player cannot find a place for their punctuation, they miss a turn. If a player places punctuation wrongly (in the opinion of the majority or by appeal to the teacher), they miss a turn. The winner is the player who uses up his or her cards first.

Follow-up

- Another way to use the cards is for the pack (the cards used above, or a different pack designed to suit the stage of development of each group) to be shuffled, dealt and held face down. A simple pack may contain no inverted commas, a more difficult one might include dashes, hyphens, semi-colons, etc. Players then take the top card of their pack and lay it face down in front of player one. He or she then has to make up a sentence using that punctuation (plus any other needed to complete what he or she writes). A point is scored if the punctuation is correctly used. Play rotates around the group until all the cards are used up.
- After playing these games, the children could use what they have learned to check each other's punctuation. This could be done using another game format as follows:
  - full stops are worth one point
  - commas two points
  - question and exclamation marks three points
  - inverted commas four points.
- The checker awards marks for each piece of punctuation correctly used, but deducts marks where punctuation is missing or wrongly used. This game will help to motivate the children to take more care with their punctuation.

Punctuation Cards

Passage to Punctuate

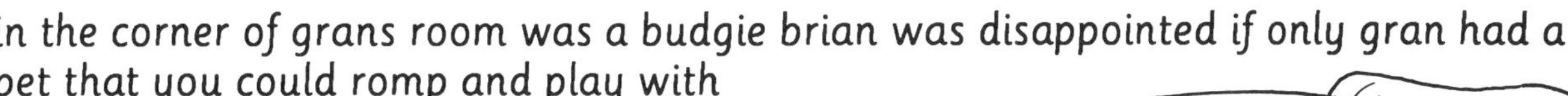

in the corner of grans room was a budgie brian was disappointed if only gran had a pet that you could romp and play with

whats he called asked brian

i just call him budgie said gran

hello budgie said brian

budgie said nothing

cant he talk asked brian

he can when he wants to said gran but youve got to put a bit of life into it

granny puckered her lips and said in a wheedling tone of voice whos a pretty boy then

budgie nodded and repeated the words in a thin scratchy voice like an old gramophone pretty boy pretty boy pretty boy

granny smiled you try it brian i'm going to make a cup of tea

brian tried it just like gran whos a pretty boy then

budgie said nothing

boring muttered Brian himself

Im not boring exclaimed budgie

brian stared in amazement you can talk he gasped

PUNCTUATION CARDS

capital letter	capital letter	capital letter	capital letter	capital letter	capital letter	capital letter
●	●	●	●	●	●	●
,	,	,	,	,	,	,
“ ”	“ ”	“ ”	“ ”	“ ”	“ ”	“ ”
’	’	’	’	?	?	!

Punctuation Puzzlers - Ideas Page

Background

When punctuation is used well it can help clarify the meaning of a piece of writing, and can even be used to change meaning. This activity page uses some fun activities to help the children explore this for themselves.

Follow-up

Other fun examples for the children might be:

- A prisoner found his death warrant. It read:
  EXECUTE. NO REPRIEVE.
  How could he change the punctuation to save his life?
  - The prisoner changed the full stop to a question mark and placed a full stop after 'no'. The warrant then read:
    EXECUTE? NO. REPRIEVE.
- An American gangster was asked if he wanted a fistful of money, i.e. **ten dollar notes.**
  By putting a hyphen in the right place he managed to receive more money. How?
  - **ten dollar-notes** (value only ten dollars)
  - **ten-dollar notes** (plural – must have been at least twenty dollars).

Activities

- The nonsense poems on the activity page make sense if commas are added in the correct place in each line.
- Ask the children to write their own nonsense poems to test other members of the class. Some children will have no difficulty writing their own punctuation nonsense poem, but others may need help. The following pattern will help the children to write such a poem without becoming completely confused.

what you saw	what he/she/it was doing

cut and slide

The children write 'sensible' sentences in this grid. When it is full, they cut it down the dotted line and slide the right hand side up one line. Then they add short phrases at the beginning and end to finish the poem. Some more able children may even be able to write a poem that rhymes.

- A valuable follow-up to this section is reading the poems aloud, stressing that pauses should be guided by punctuation and line layout, not by line ending.
- The signpost can be given a totally opposite meaning by inserting the following punctuation:

DANGER?
NO. SWIMMING ALLOWED.

Punctuation Puzzlers

Read these two nonsense poems aloud.

Upside Down Caesar

Caesar entered on his head
A helmet on each foot
A sandal in his hand he had
His trusty sword to boot.

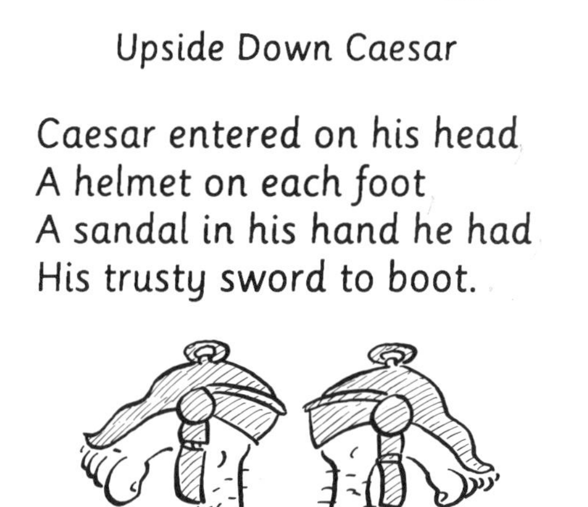

The Hungry Pack of Cards

I saw a pack of cards gnawing a bone
I saw a dog seated on Britain's throne
I saw the Queen shut up in a box
I saw an orange driving a fat ox
I saw a butcher not a fortnight old
I saw a greatcoat all of solid gold
I saw two buttons talking of their lives
I saw two friends who told it to their wives.

- Make the poems sensible by adding commas.

Two workmen had travelled forty miles to the beach with a new signpost. They spent all afternoon digging a hole when, to their horror, they found they had brought the wrong sign. The sign read:

but the beach was quite safe. Luckily one of the men had a brilliant idea. They had no paint, but with his pen he placed some punctuation in the sign which completely changed its meaning. What do you think he put?

Taking It Further

Several items of punctuation, e.g. the semi-colon, have not been dealt with on separate pages. There are two reasons for this.

- First is the tendency towards a lighter use of punctuation in modern English. For example, secretaries are now taught to use 'open' punctuation for business letters in which all punctuation in addresses is omitted, there is no comma after 'Dear Sir', and the letter itself uses the very minimum of punctuation. The colon and semi-colon are so little used today that their use can look affected.
- Secondly, the punctuation covered in this book represents challenge enough for most children of junior age. The few who need to go beyond this can be dealt with individually by the teacher.

A few brief notes follow on more advanced aspects of punctuation that might be usefully taught as the need arises.

COLON

A colon is used to signal that further information follows: a list or an additional phrase or clause. This technique is often combined with bulleted points (see 'Bullets'). The most common use of the colon today is to introduce a list, e.g. the house included the following: a lounge, a kitchen with several new appliances, two large bedrooms, a bathroom.

SEMI-COLON

The semi-colon shows co-ordination between clauses. It is difficult to teach its more sophisticated uses without also teaching a course on clause analysis. It can be explained to the children as a more forceful comma. They can be taught one of its simpler uses, the punctuation of complex lists, e.g.

On my desk there is a computer with its monitor, disk drive and printer; a bust of J.S. Bach, who is my favourite composer; an assortment of pens, pencils and rulers; and a great pile of papers that need sorting out.

Since several commas are used in this list, for sub-lists, etc. semi-colons have been used to separate the main items.

BULLETS

Bullets are increasingly used to make informational writing clearer. Often the bulleted points are introduced with a sentence ending with a colon. There are two important points to remember:

- the text following the bullet should read on naturally from the introductory sentence
- the text should begin with a small letter since in English (as opposed to American) usage, a colon is not followed by a capital letter. If there is no introductory sentence, the bulleted points can begin with a capital letter.

HYPHEN

The main use of the hyphen is to join two words to show that they stand for one thing. The best example, and the most important to teach, is the use of the hyphen in numbers: e.g. twenty-four (two words, but one number). There are many words which, strictly speaking, require hyphens, e.g. 'Anglo-Saxon' and these should be taught as the need arises. Another use of hyphenation is to break words at the right-hand margin. Words should be broken only at syllable division. Above all, discourage the children from using a hyphen just to put the last letter on the next line!

Taking It Further

THE DASH

Dashes can be used instead of commas in certain instances to give a more dramatic effect – but should not be over-used! They can also be added to a colon to introduce a list (:–) but this is considered old-fashioned.

BRACKETS

Brackets are used to insert additional information (like this). The phrase or clause in brackets does not begin or end with punctuation of its own. If the brackets fall at the end of a sentence, the final full stop is placed outside the brackets. The practice of using brackets as a neat way of crossing out (the mistake is enclosed in brackets) should not be encouraged, as brackets have their own proper purpose. The children should be taught to cross out with a neat line through the middle of the text.

UNDERLINING

This is used in manuscripts to emphasise titles and subheadings. It is also used as a substitute for italics which in printed texts are used to give emphasis. Children should be taught to underline with a single line drawn with a ruler. When children are using the word-processor, they should use **bold type** for titles and subheadings and *italics* for emphasis.

TYPEFACES

Printed manuscripts use different styles and sizes of typeface to help clarify meaning, in a similiar way to punctuation. Use of typefaces can be explored by studying a wide range of books, magazines and newspapers and by experimentation on a word-processor or with a desktop publishing package.

AUDIENCE AND PURPOSE

Appropriateness to audience and purpose is just as much a criterion for punctuation as for content. A business letter will be differently punctuated from a personal letter, a typed letter will differ in certain aspects of punctuation from a handwritten one. Informal writing will contain more contractions than formal writing. Some printed novels will use single inverted commas for dialogue, though the convention for handwriting is to use double inverted commas. All these points can be assimilated by children who are taught to read actively, i.e. to examine a text to see how it achieves its effects, through ideas, vocabulary, grammar and punctuation. They will then be able to use these features creatively – not just to avoid mistakes, but to use punctuation to achieve artistic effects.

Eight ways to help ...

There are hundreds of ideas in this book to enable you to develop and extend the photocopiable pages. Here are just eight ways to help you make the most of the Ideas Bank series.

Photocopy a page, paste on to card and laminate/cover with sticky-backed plastic to use with groups. The children can now write on the pages using water-based pens which can be washed off.

2

Photocopy on to both sides of the paper, and put another useful activity on the back. Develop a simple filing system so that your colleagues can find relevant sheets and do not duplicate them again.

3

Save the sheets – if the children do not have to cut them up as a part of the activity – and re-use them. Label the sets, and keep them safely in files.

4

Make the most of group work. Children working in small groups need one sheet to discuss between them.

5

Put the sheets inside clear plastic wallets. This means the sheets are easily stored in a binder and will last longer. Again, the children's writing can be wiped away.

6

Use the activity page as an ideas page for yourself. Discuss issues with the class and ask the children to produce artwork and writing.

Make an overhead transparency of the page. You and your colleagues can now use the idea time and time again.

Ask yourself, "Does every child in this class/group need to deal with/work through this activity page?". If not, don't photocopy it!

